The H
Comic Annual

CW00421526

Martin Hamer

Martin Hamer

Published by
Hamer 20th Century Books

Front cover by kind permission of Express Newspapers
Back cover by kind permission of DC Thomson Ltd
Colour plates in this Supplement and the original Guide by kind
permission of DC Thomson, Disney Enterprises, Express
Newspapers and IPC Magazines on behalf of Amalgamated
Press, Fleetway and themselves
Grateful acknowledgement is made to the original artists

This Supplement first published in UK 2002
by Hamer 20th Century Books
Station House Auction Rooms, Carlton Road,
Worksop, S81 7AG England
Tel 01909 479989 or 01909 569428
Email martinhamer@btconnect.com
www.hamerauctions.co.uk

Printed and bound in Worksop UK by Bayliss Printing Ltd

The Hamer Comic Annual Guide No 2 Supplementary Update

The Hamer Comic Annual Guide No 2 Supplementary Update is of most value when read alongside The Hamer Comic Annual Guide No 1 which was published in 2000. However the Supplement can simply be read on its own merits as a document containing the latest market developments for the collector and dealer.

You will realise that the prices given are in almost every case prices paid by real people. All auction prices and dates quoted are from Hamer Auctions over the past two years. And in every case the purchaser has paid a premium on top. We only give the hammer price which is therefore a Conservative estimate. If you want the New Labour or Liberal Dem price – the proper price in other words - add 15%.

Follow a Stable in Form

I am a keen horse racing supporter and when I get time I check back through the formbook and examine races which I believe will throw up a winner or two. I highlight in a colour code horses according to how they have progressed. So if I'm looking at a race from a couple of months ago and the horse won next time out I mark it in green. If it ran second that's orange, third is pink and unplaced is red. The more green the better the race the more red the worse. I recommend you take a highlighter to the original Guide. If the Supplement shows a book to have risen in value mark it in green. If it's stayed the same highlight it in orange or if it's fallen red. That way you will have an at-a-glance verdict on the way the market is going and you'll know where to put your money. Some will say the monetary value of their collection is immaterial – well enjoy the Guide anyway but you'll miss out on a lot of colouring.

The analogy extends further. Just as conditions affect the way horses run, you shouldn't be put off by the fact that a book valued at £400 in VG (Say Good to Firm) sells at only £200 in Good (Say Soft).

News from Hamer Auction Rooms

In May 2000 we auctioned the rare brown-faced printing of 1973 Rupert Annual. I had valued this book at £5,000 in VG condition only three months earlier when The Hamer Guide was first published. The hammer came down at £16,500 to a packed and stunned auction room. Admittedly the book was a Fine example. The resultant publicity was international – I was even interviewed on Armed Forces Radio and Eastern Australia's breakfast show – they phoned me at 11pm when I was half way through a bottle of Pinot Grigio but I think I made sense. Surely now another copy of this book would emerge on to the market.

Like us nearly every bookseller in the country had been plagued with calls from people who thought they had the rare book. After articles in The Times and practically every other national newspaper the publishers received thousands of calls - all I'm afraid false alarms. And then a caller assured us he had the correct printing. It had been bought at a Dulwich College bring and buy sale in the 1980's for a few pence. I made the necessary checks over the phone, became convinced and set out to London to meet the vendor's agent at his club.

The book was pulled from a briefcase and it was a surprisingly VG bright example, not price clipped but with the previous owner's name Thomas childishly inscribed. We decided to discuss the matter of estimate and reserve over lunch. I must confess I was a little concerned when the agent checked his briefcase into the cloakroom. He was given I remember ticket No 18 and I was convinced someone would shortly arrive to check out a similar-looking briefcase with ticket No 81. The start of a Marx Bros movie no doubt. All was well however and we agreed an estimate of £8,000.

Promoting the October 2000 sale of the book was not an easy matter. The press after all were less interested now that the market in this rarity had just increased by 100% and collectors began to say that other books must be on the point of appearing. We advertised the sale with the slogan The Brown out of the Blue but we were unable to allay fears of a mini-glut and in short the book did not reach its reserve. If the book had turned up a few years later it would undoubtedly have sold for a premium. And now 18 months down the line where are the others?

More Rupert Activity

We have solved another Rupert Bear problem since I last wrote. The Hamer Comic Annual Guide No 1 refers to the scarce Music Book No 2 and the more common Rupert Activity Book No 2 both published by Odhams in 1959. The existence of No 1 in either of these titles was a matter for conjecture but one imagined this was a project abandoned by the publishers for some reason. In March 2001 we had the answer and discovered at a fair Rupert Music and Activity Book No 1 in a single volume. It sold in our May 2001

Comic Book Auction for £1,600. So in the space of a year we had cracked two weighty nuts without even wielding a hammer – other than a gavel of course.

The Cuckoo Has Landed

In October 2000 we took delivery of the massive collection of the Late Mr Denis Gifford and were invited to sell that collection on behalf of the administrators of his estate. The stuff arrived on a groaning lorry. It was housed in some 600 boxes and weighed around 10 tons. It had taken almost a month to empty the terraced house. Comics were found all over the place - even in the oven. We found ourselves almost squeezed out of our own newly renovated premises at Worksop Station.

We knew that Mr Gifford had a great pal in Bob Monkhouse OBE so we approached the celebrated comedian and game show host to write the foreword for the first auction catalogue which he kindly agreed to do. Bob was a year younger than Denis and they met at Dulwich College about 35 years before the Rupert turned up in the same buildings.

At the time of writing we have held six Denis Gifford sales and another four are scheduled for 2002 before the comics, books, artwork and ephemera are finally dispersed. Catalogues are available from ourselves and constitute a remarkable series documenting the biggest collection in the UK ever to be offered on sale.

The Denis Gifford collection has obviously had a big impact on informing this Supplement. It has also had a great influence on the prices for future buyers and sellers.

Colour Plates and Images

All books for which cover images are provided in this Supplement and the original Hamer Guide are from our own stock or from private collections. They represent books we have sold over the years. Obviously the copyright for the books themselves rests with the publishers and the artists. The photographs in this Supplement were all commissioned by Hamer 20th Century Books. The Hamer Comic Annual Guide No 1 contains 13 colour plates which provide at-a-glance identification for early Dandy, Beano, Mickey Mouse and Rupert Bear annuals. We have retained a few hundred copies for sale.

Condition

You will see distinct differences in price for relatively minor distinctions in grade. For details of how to recognise condition see The Hamer Comic Annual Guide No 1.

Acknowledgements

I did ask for help in the original Guide and I am very grateful for the contributions from Ray Moore, Dave Bailey, Roger Coombes, Brian Northam, Tony Wright, John Swan, Alan Thomas, Graham Stewart and B Estick. Anyone wishing to assist with information for The Hamer Comic Annual Guide No 3 which I intend to be a complete re-write in 2004 is most welcome to contact me.

My grateful thanks go to Express Newspapers for permission to reproduce the Rupert Bear covers and DC Thomson for the Magic and Broons images. And once again to Disney Enterprises Inc., IPC Magazines and DC Thomson for the images in the original Guide.

Martin Hamer

The word Annual is omitted from book titles in this Supplement. All comments represent amendments to The Hamer Comic Annual Guide No 1.

Adventure Land
1924 No 1 VG/Fine £50 August 2001
1925, 1926 & 1929 G/VG £40 August 2001
1925 Reading copy & 1934 G/VG £42 April 2001
1927 VG in VG d/w £30 August 2001
1929 VG £17 August 2001
1937, 1939 & 1940 G/VG £45 August 2001

Adventure Comic Paper
Dixon Hawke was the star detective attraction and is now correctly spelt.
1920's Christmas issues x 5 Good only £40 October 2001
1932 – 1939 Christmas issues Good plus £55 October 2001
1940 – 1957 Christmas issues G/VG £55 October 2001

Adventure Story Comic
Published by Odhams
No 1 (Undated but probably 1959/60) VG £25 February 2001

Ally Sloper

Ally Sloper's Half Holiday No 1 from May 3rd 1884 in Good only condition made a staggering £3600 in our April 2001 sale. I do not offer this as a recommended retail price as quite clearly two people were utterly determined to gain the prize. However I wouldn't expect the paper to sell for under four figures if another one were to surface.

21 issues 1884 – 1922 Good only £140 February 2001
Ally Sloper ceramic ash tray £60 October 2001
Ally Sloper & Mrs Sloper x 2 brass hearth stands £130 February 2001
Ally Sloper Toby jug £90 February 2001

In the four issues of the Ally Sloper Magazine published by Denis Gifford 1976 – 1977, Ally was drawn by Walter Bell. Frank Hampson and Frank Bellamy contributed to the magazine but neither drew Sloper.

American Comics

300 lots of Golden Age American comics made a hammer price of £54,700 in our June 2001 sale. For full details and prices realised order the back catalogues for June & August 2001 from Hamer 20th Century Books.

Andy Capp

Original pen & ink strip by Reg Smythe VG £75 February 2001

Andy Pandy

Clark Brandt print 1971 VG is worth around £20

Archie Andrews

Painting Book 1950's VG plus £32 December 2001

Arthur Askey

1940 Taped spine Good only £25 May 2000, Nr VG £35 December 2000, Signed VG £160 August 2001

Avengers

A number of people were in touch on this topic. The first couple of TV series featured Ian Hendry with Patrick MacNee and then Honor Blackman as Cathy Gale. Diana Rigg first appeared as Emma Peel in 1964 and not 1961 as I previously believed. Even more light was thrown on the subject by another correspondent. Ian Hendry played David Keel in the first series. Cathy Gale was in Series 2 and 3 and Diana Rigg had to wait until Series 4 which began on 2nd October 1965. Also the first annual appeared in 1967 and not 1969 as I previously believed.

Batman Comic
World Adventure Library No 1 1966 VG with Superman No 1 1967 VG Both published by WDL £25 April 2001

Battler Britton
Novels VG in d/ws 1961 & 1962 £25 August 2001.

Beano Book – See Colour Plates in Hamer Comic Annual Guide No 1
1940 No 1 Slightly less than VG £2,500 October 2000, Good only £1,750 April 2001

1941 Less than VG £500 October 2000, Reading copy £320 April 2001, Good only £410 November 2001

1942 Fine £1,400 May 2000, Fine £1,600 October 2000

Magic-Beano Book
1943 Nr VG £1600 October 2000, G/VG £950 May 2001
1944 VG £250 October 2000
1945 VG £250 October 2000, VG £380 April 2001
1946 Nr VG £300 October 2000, G/VG £600 May 2001
1947 VG £280 October 2000, Good plus £140 September 2001
1948 VG May 2000 £150, Fine £250 October 2000, G/VG £150 May 2001, VG/Fine £260 April 2001, Good £100 November 2001

1949 Nr VG £100 October 2000, VG/Fine £200 April 2001, VG plus £140 July 2001

1950 VG/Fine £250 May 2000, VG/Fine £300 April 2001

Beano Book
1951 VG plus £90 October 2000, Fine £340 April 2001, Good £85 November 2001

1951 – 1954 VG £200 May 2001
1952 Fine £60 October 2000
1953 VG £40 October 2000, VG £52 October 2000, Good plus £37 April 2001, Good plus £37 November 2001

1954 Fine £95 October 2000, G/VG £25 October 2000, £80 VG/Fine May 2001
1955 G/VG £45 October 2000, G/VG £35 April 2001
1956 VG/Fine £60 October 2000
1957 G/VG £45 October 2000, VG £75 October 2000
1958 VG plus £55 October 2000, VG £65 May 2001, G/VG £55
November 2001

1959 G/VG £35 October 2000, VG/Fine £75 October 2000
1959 & 1960 Both VG £45 May 2000
1960 VG £70 November 2001
1960 – 1969 VG plus collection £490 October 2000
1960 VG/Fine £70 May 2001
1965 G/VG £20 October 2000
1966 VG plus £25 October 2000
1968 Fine £37 October 2000
1969 VG £22 October 2000
1970, 1971 & 1972 Fine £32 October 2000
1970 – 1999 Complete run Mostly Mint £150 October 2000

Beano Comic
Flyer announcing imminent publication of the Beano VG plus £200 August 2001
No 1 30th July 1938 Trimmed £1,550 February 2001
No 12 G/VG £110 February 2001
No 18 Good only £62 September 2001
Nos 68 G/VG, 110 Good, 109, 351, 453, 481 & 605 Good plus £90
September 2001

1939 Christmas VG £80 February 2001
1943 10 issues Fine £260 & 9 issues Fine £260 February 2001
1943 Christmas issue Fine £90 February 2001
1944 Complete year in bound volume VG/Fine £340 April 2001
1945 Complete year in bound volume VG/Fine £220 April 2001
1946 Complete year in bound volume VG/Fine £220 April 2001
1947 Nos 308 & 324 G/VG £22 October 2000
1949 Complete year in bound volume VG/Fine £340 April 2001
1950 Nos 411 – 441 in bound volume VG/Fine £180 April 2001
1950's 9 Christmas issues G/VG £75 October 2001
In April 2001 we also offered bound volumes in which Beano and Dandy comics
were combined. Late 1940's and 1950's thus made around £3 per issue.

Beezer

1958 Nr VG £70 October 2000, VG plus £75 May 2001
1959 VG £15 October 2000
1960's Complete run VG plus £55 December 2000

Beezer Comics

No 1, Good £47 August 2001, Good only £75 September 2001, VG £110 November 2001
No 2 VG £60 October 2001
Christmas issues x 19 1950's - 1970's G/VG £60 October 2001

Beryl the Peril

1959 VG plus £75 October 2000, Repaired spine £40 October 2000
1959, 1961, 1965, 1967 & 1969 G/VG £100 October 2000

Billy and Bunny

1928 G/VG £20 August 2001
1930 VG £15 August 2001
1933 & 1937 Reading copies & 1938 G/VG £15 August 2001
1938 & 1949 Reading copies & 1950 VG £17 August 2001
1948 Billy and Bunny being pulled through water in a wooden tub by a goose
1949 Billy and Bunny on a swing with Puck about to cut the rope

Bimbo Comic

No 1 18th March 1961 Fine £22 February 2001

Birthday Fun

VG £8 each April 2001

Black Bob

The artistic creation of Jack Prout first appeared in The Dandy on November 25th 1944. Stories were written by Bill Swinton, Ron Caird and David Tarrie amongst others.
1949 G/VG £40 December 2000
1961 & 1965 Both Fine £60 May 2000

Blackhawk

See TV Boardman

Bliss Comic

No 1 VG March 4th 1961 £32 February 2001

Blue Peter
1964 No 1 VG £100 October 2000

Bonzo
Bonzo Laughter Annual 1935 VG £170 February 2001
Bonzo Annual 1947 G/VG £35 April 2001, VG £35 November 2001
Bonzo's Book of Stories 1951 Good plus £30 November 2001
Bonzo Great Big Midget Book published by Dean 1934 Covers detached £47 April 2001
Bonzo's Painting Book pub Dean 1930's G/VG £42 February 2001
Bonzo Playful Animals Fine £50 February 2001
Bonzo books published in France by Hachette in the 1940's VG £40 each February 2001
New Bonzo Book published by Partridge in 1927 Poor £24 April 2001
The Bonzooloo Book published by Partridge in 1929 Poor £30 April 2001

Original Studdy watercolour Fine £2,300 February 2001
Portfolios G/VG £200 each February 2001
Bonzo Glass ashtray made in Czechoslovakia £100 October 2001

Bookano Books
No 5 VG plus with flyer for Book 4 £60 November 2001

Boys' Cinema Paper
No 1 Good only £60 October 2001
1920 – 1939 x 200 issues Good £380 October 2001
1928 – 1936 G/VG £2 each February 2001

Boys' Friend Libraries
There has been a great upsurge in interest in Biggles due mainly to expatriate buyers on the Internet and these pocket sized comic papers are an early 1930's source of WE Johns Biggles material. There are Biggles stories in Nos 617, 621, 625, 630 & 701 and we sold a very poor collection of those numbers – some with back covers missing - in April 2001 for £230. Interestingly we know of a buyer prepared to pay four figures for each of them in VG/Fine. Do they exist in such condition I wonder?
79 issues from 1930's Non–Biggles content Good £445 August 2001

Boys' Fun
1954 & 1955 VG £10 each April 2001

Boys' Herald Papers
1919 G/VG £3 each February 2001

Boy's Own
1922 VG £32 December 2000

British 6d & 1/- Comic Reprints of American comics
Comics which would not sell at £3 each three years ago are now making up to £20 each at auction. See Miller/Fawcett

Broons, The
1940's There were two Broons jig-saws produced – paper shortages made them cheaper to produce than annuals. The Broons family at home with chidren playing on the carpet Fine with box £600 May 2001

1952 Fine £250 May 2000, Good only £85 November 2001
1956 VG £37 October 2000
1958 Good only & 1960 VG £30 October 2000
1962, 1964 & 1966 All Fine £90 October 2000
1964 VG £32 November 2001

Bruin Boys
1929 G/VG, 1932 Good & 1940 VG/Fine in d/w £70 December 2000

Bubbles
1924 Good plus £27 September 2001
1939, 1942 & 1943 Good plus £15 August 2001

Bubbles Comic
Nos 64 – 90 in 1922 bound volume VG £10 April 2001

Buck Ryan
See Super Detective Library

Buffalo Bill Wild West
Nos 7, 8 & 9 All VG in d/ws £30 December 2000
No 9 VG in VG d/w £15 November 2001

Buffalo Bill Comics and Papers
See Miller/Fawcett & TV Boardman

Bunter

Original pen & ink for Holiday Annual by CH Chapman made £410 February 2001 & a Frank Minnitt pen & ink original for Knockout made £160 at the same sale.

Bunty Book for Girls

Bunty was drawn by Doris Kinnear.

Bunty Comics

Big Upsurge in interest at last!
No 1 18th January 1958 Fine £65 each February 2001
1958 – 1968 VG £3 each February 2001
1950's & 1960's x 100 issues G/VG £145 November 2001

Buster Book

Buster was the son of Andy Capp but I am reliably informed had nothing to do with the former's artist Reg Smythe. He was in fact drawn by Bill Titcombe until February 1961 when the link with Andy Capp was dropped. Subsequently drawn by Hugh McNeill, Angel Nadal, Reg Parlett and Jimmy Hansen.

Buster Comic

No 1 28th May 1960 VG £70 August 2001

Butterfly Comic

No 1 September 17th 1904 Good £40 August 2001
1904 Bound volume Nos 1 – 16 VG £130 August 2001
Ten bound volumes between 1908 & 1940 Earliest brittle, rest VG £330 April 2001

1937 Coronation issue VG £15 September 2001
360 issues between 1904 & 1940 Good £235 October 2001

Champion Annual for Boys

Rockfist Rogan appeared in at least three novels written by Hal Wilton originally for the paper and published by Stuart Pepper. We sold three VG in d/ws for £85 in April 2001.
1924 G/VG £15 September 2001
1929, 1935, 1938 & 1939 Good plus £50 August 2001
1936 G/VG £15 December 2000
1951, 1953 & 1955 Good plus £7 August 2001

Champion Comic Paper
Bound volume July – December 1938 VG/Fine £100 August 2001

Chatterbox
1927 VG in original d/w £27 with another ordinary book
April 2001

Cheerio Comic
Bound volumes Nos 1 – 49 & Kinema Comic (Title change 21st April 1920)
Nos 2 – 10 G/VG £280 August 2001

Cheyenne
1962 (A Television Storybook – Newtown) Estimated at £12

Chicks Own Comic
No 1 September 25th 1920 Good plus £60 August 2001
1926 – 1954 x 20 Christmas issues £50 October 2001

Chips Comic (Illustrated Chips)
No 1 July 26th 1890 Reading copy £5 August 2001
Three VG bound volumes from the late 1930's & early 1940's £40 April 2001

Chuckles Comic
No 1 January 10th 1914 G/VG £60 August 2001

Chummy Book
1923 Fine £26 May 2000

Classics Illustrated
Prices are for UK first editions in VG/Fine August 2001
No 143 Sail with the Devil £55
No 146 Baron Munchausen £55
No 147 Through the Looking Glass £55
No 148 Night of Terror £55
No 149 The Gorilla Hunters £45
No 150 The Canterville Ghost £40
No 156 The Dog Crusoe £55
No 157 Queen of Spades £55
No 159 Master and Man £55
No 161 The Aeneid £65
No 162 Saga of the North £55

Reprints x 9 including Frankenstein £70
Reprints x 11 including Alice in Wonderland £65

Classics in Pictures
Nos 1 – 12 pub Amex at 1/6 VG £100 February 2001

Cococubs
Published by Cadburys
1936 & 1950 G/VG £100 February 2001

Cococub News
1936 – 1939 Nos 2 – 34 Good £130 October 2001

Comet Comic
Bound volume 1952 – 1953 Nos 193 – 258 Fine £110 February 2001

Comicolour
1947 – 1956 G/VG £100 April 2001
1947, 1948, 1950, 1952, 1953, 1955 & 1956 Good plus £60 September 2001

Comic Cuts
No 1 May 17th 1890 G/VG £290 August 2001
1948 Complete year together with complete years for Chips & Wonder in a
single bound volume VG £40 April 2001.
Nos 2929 – 3006 1951 – 1953 in single bound volume VG/Fine £30 April 2001
29 x Holiday issues Good £80 October 2001

Cowboy Book for Boys
1937 VG plus £30 April 2001

Cowboy Comic (Cowboy Picture Library)
Between Nos 147 & 256 G/VG £5 each April 2001
Between Nos 88 & 253 G/VG 30 issues £130 November 2001

Cracker Comic
No 1 x 4 issues 1975 Mint without gifts £26 November 2001

Crackers
Alex Akerbladh – correct spelling
1940 VG in VG d/w £95 December 2000

Crasher
Published by Kayebon in the 1940's
7 issues inc No 1 VG plus £35 February 2001

Curly Wee
1940's VG & 5 reading copies £25 October 2001
1950 VG £10 October 2001

Cute Fun
1948, 1949 1950, 1952 (2), 1953 – 1956 G/VG £55 September 2001

Daily Express Children's
See Rupert Bear

Dalek
Outer Space Book 1965 Fine £50 October 2000

Dan Dare - Hawk Books at a premium
Pilot of the Future De Luxe 1987 Fine £80 September 2001
Pilot of the Future Volume 2 1988 Fine £75 September 2001
Pilot of the Future Volume 3 1989 Fine £140 September 2001
Pilot of the Future Volume 4 1990 Fine £110 September 2001
Pilot of the Future Volume 5 1991 Fine £90 September 2001
Pilot of the Future Volume 6 1992 Fine £55 September 2001
Pilot of the Future Volume 7 1993 Fine £30 September 2001
Pilot of the Future Volume 8 1993 Fine £30 September 2001
Pilot of the Future Volume 9 1994 Fine £32 September 2001
Pilot of the Future Volume 10 1994 Fine £20 September 2001
Pilot of the Future Volume 11 1995 Fine £20 September 2001
Pilot of the Future Volume 12 1995 Fine £35 September 2001
Dan Dare Dossier 1990 with four of the soft covered Eagle reprints Fine £37 April 2001
Dan Dare Dossier 1990 Fine £65 September 2001

Interplanetary Stamp Album VG/Fine £170 in May 2000
Walkie-Talkie by Randall in bright box £90 February 2001
Dan Dare Ingersoll pocket watch £200 in G/VG July 2001
Spaceship Kite Good £140 December 2000

Dandy, The - See Colour Plates in Hamer Guide No 1
Dudley Watkins also drew the strips for Oliver Twist, Kidnapped Good sans

d/w £10 April 2001, Treasure Island VG in VG d/w £80 April 2001 & Robinson Crusoe G/VG in G/VG d/w £35 April 2001 published by DC Thomson & John Leng in d/ws in the late 1940's. Morgyn The Mighty by the same artist and publishers VG in d/w £47 December 2000 & VG in chipped d/w £55 April 2001.

Dandy Monster Comic
1939 Fine £2500 October 2000, Good only £700 April 2001, G/VG £950 May 2001

1940 Good only £200 May 2000, VG plus £500 October 2000, VG £420 April 2001, G/VG £550 May 2001, Fine £1000 November 2001

1941 Nr VG £400 October 2000, G/VG £360 May 2001
1942 VG £350 October 2000, G/VG £200 April 2001, Restored VG £310 September 2001

1943 VG £210 December 2000, G/VG £950 May 2001, Restored VG £260 September 2001

1944 VG £380 October 2000, Reading copy £42 April 2001, G/VG £210 September 2001

1945 G/VG £230 October 2000, G/VG £150 April 2001, VG £320 May 2001
1946 VG £230 October 2000, VG £310 May 2001, G/VG £170 October 2001
1947 VG £110 December 2000, Good plus £105 September 2001, VG £200 October 2001, G/VG £160 November 2001

1948 VG £130 May 2001
1949 VG/Fine £160 October 2000, VG plus £210 April 2001
1950 Fine £240 April 2001, VG/Fine £90 July 2001
1951 Fine £200 April 2001, VG £45 November 2001
1952 G/VG £37 April 2001

Dandy Book
1954 Fine £65 July 2001, VG £40 November 2001
1955 VG plus £40 November 2001
1955 – 1959 G/VG £90 October 2000
1956 Fine £120 April 2001
1960's Complete run VG £240 December 2000
1961 Fine £45 May 2000

1965 & 1966 VG £20 October 2000
1967 Fine £23 May 2000, Fine £20 October 2000
1968 Fine £45 October 2000
1969 Fine £22 May 2000, Fine £27 October 2000
1970, 1971 & 1972 All Fine £25 October 2000

Dandy Comic
Flyer announcing imminent publication of the Dandy VG plus £150 August 2001
1938 Christmas VG £100 February 2001
1939 Christmas with 2 others Good plus £190 October 2001
1942 Christmas VG £65 February 2001
1944 – 1945 Nos 259 – 308 & No 269 Keyhole Kate to the front cover VG
£320 April 2001

1946 – 1947 Complete years in bound volume VG £320 April 2001
1949 Complete year in bound volume VG/Fine £200 April 2001
1947 Christmas VG £50 February 2001
1950 Complete year in bound volume VG/Fine £100 April 2001
1967 & 1970 Full years VG £140 November 2001

Dennis the Menace
1956 G/VG £60 October 2000
1960, 1962, 1964, 1966 & 1968 VG £70 October 2000

Desperate Dan
1954 VG £90 May 2000, Good plus £50 September 2001, G/VG £105
October 2001, G/VG £70 November 2001

Dick Boss, The Adventures of
These small books by Maz and published by Literary Press are numbered 1 &
2. We sold them both in one lot VG £180 April 2001.

Dixon Hawke Case Book
Published by DC Thomson in soft covers Nos 1 & 3 Good £130 August 2001

Donald Duck
1940 Worm damaged £130 February 2001
Birn Brothers with a lovely pictorial spine 1937 VG/Fine £50 April 2001.

Eagle
Nos 1 VG, 2 & 4 VG in d/ws £50 October 2000

Nos 1 & 2 G/VG £60 May 2001

Eagle Books
Anastasia Jet Plane Press-Out Fine £27 February 2001
Book of Magic 1956 G/VG £75 in February 2001
The Happy Warrior (Comic strip life story of Sir Winston Churchill)
published by Hulton 1958 VG £25 April 2001, VG plus £40 November 2001

Eagle Novels
Four books in d/ws including Dan Dare on Mars published by Hulton Press
in 1956 and a copy of Eagle Special Investigator sans d/w All G/VG £100
April 2001

Eagle Comic
Bound volume April – October 1950 Nos 1 – 26 VG/Fine £400 August 2001
First volume Mainly G/VG £430 May 2000, Reading copies lacking 6 issues
£105 May 2000

Volume 1 Nos 1 – 50 bound (No 1 Good only – others VG) £400 May 2001
Nos 2 – 21 G/VG £110 September 2001
Volume 1 Nos 27 - 52 & Volume 2 Nos 1 – 26 in single bound volume VG/Fine
£130 April 2001

Volume 2 Good plus £50 May 2000
Volume 3 G/VG & lacking 2 issues £42 May 2000
Volumes 4 & 5 G/VG & lacking 2 issues £60 May 2000
Volume 6 Bound VG £70 May 2001
Volumes 6 & 7 VG £100 May 2000
Volume 7 VG £100 October 2000
Volumes 8, 9 & 10 lacking 4 issues £100 May 2000

Enid Blyton's
Worth mentioning that in our May 2000 auction we sold Five on Kirrin Island
1947 1st Edition VG in worn d/w for £180. Five Go To Smugglers Top 1945
1st Edition & Five Go Adventuring Again 1943 1st Edition both VG in worn
d/ws made £600. The Castle of Adventure and Valley of Adventure 1946 &
1947 1sts respectively VG in VG d/ws made £390.

1933 & 1934 Nos 1 & 2 News Chronicle Girls & Boys Story Books G/VG £45
October 2000

Express Super Colour
1959 VG £20 October 2001

Fairies Album
1944 – 1957 G/VG £8 each April 2001

Favourite Comic
No 1 January 21st 1911 Reading copy £13 August 2001

Fawcett 6d & 1/- reprints of US comics
See Miller

Felix
No 1 published by Hulton 1925 Good only £27 April 2001
1926 Good £40 April 2001
Felix the Cat Book published by McLaughlin in USA 1927 Reading copy £80
April 2001

Film Fun
1938 No 1 Good £40 August 2001
1939 VG £90 August 2001
1940 Reading copy £25 August 2001
1941 Good only £35 August 2001
1942 VG plus £75 November 2001, Good plus £85 August 2001
1943 G/VG £55 October 2000, G/VG £65 August 2001
1944 Good plus £50 August 2001
1945 G/VG £42 October 2000, Good plus £35 August 2001
1946 VG £37 October 2000, VG £40 August 2001
1947 G/VG £17 October 2000, VG £45 August 2001
1947 Good & 1952 – 1961 G/VG £125 December 2000
1948 VG £41 October 2000, VG £25 August 2001
1949 VG plus £30 August 2001
1950 – 1955 VG £50 August 2001
1956 – 1961 G/VG £30 August 2001

Film Fun Comic – See Colour Plates Hamer Guide No 1
The comic never attempted colour until flirting with green, blue, yellow and
orange borders to front and rear covers from around 1957.
Nos 2 – 24 Bound volume Good £90 April 2001
22 issues between 1928 & 1939 Good £240 February 2001
1920's & 1930's Good £4 each October 2001

1950's & 1960's Good £2 each October 2001
Between 1940 & 1951 Good only 50 issues £140 February 2001
1957 Bound volume G/VG £55 May 2001
Two comics of similar format and appearance - Film Picture Stories x 9 issues 1934 Good £45 February 2001

Kinema Comic No 1 April 24th 1920 made £280 in VG in February 2001
Kinema Comic x 10 issues Good only 1928 – 1931 £50 February 2001

Another sister paper was Sports Fun - 12 issues 1922 Good plus £40 February 2001.

Film Pictorial
1932 No 1 G/VG £50 October 2001

Film Picture Stories
See Film Fun

Fireball XL5
This was a Gerry Anderson pre-cursor of Thunderbirds.

Firefly
1915 Bound volume Nos 1 – 16 VG £150 August 2001

Flip the Frog
1931 Worn £150 February 2001, Good plus £160 September 2001, Good £95 October 2001

Set of six Flip the Frog Lyons Tea Cards 1931 VG £80 February 2001

Fresh Fun
Published by Swan 1940's
Nos 2 – 33 & 2 holiday specials G/VG £60 August 2001

Fun Book for Boys
1939 VG plus in original 90% complete d/w £25 April 2001

Funnies
1942 – 1956 G/VG £10 each April 2001
1943 – 1950 & 1952 – 1957 (Sans 1955), G/VG £50 September 2001

Funny Wonder Comic
22 x Christmas issues 1930's Good £70 October 2001

Giles
No 1 VG/Fine £150 May 2000, VG/Fine £120 May 2000, Nr VG £90
December 2000, G/VG £130 October 2000, VG/Fine £160 January 2001
No 2 VG/Fine £100 May 2000, Nr VG £150 October 2000, VG/Fine £120
January 2001
No 3 VG/Fine £100 May 2000, VG with No 8 VG £100 May 2000, VG £100
January 2001
No 4 VG/Fine £100 May 2000, Fine £120 May 2000, VG plus £120
December 2000, VG plus £120 January 2001
No 5 VG/Fine £100 May 2000, G/VG £90 October 2000, Fine £140 May
2001, VG/Fine £120 January 2001
No 6 Fine £50 May 2000, VG £50 October 2000, VG plus £42 December
2000, VG plus £40 January 2001
Nos 6 & 7 with Nurse Special All VG/Fine £100 May 2000, VG/Fine £40
January 2001
No 8 VG £22 October 2000
Nos 8 – 13 VG/Fine £60 January 2001
Nos 8 – 45 Fine £60 May 2000

Facsimiles now exist for Nos 1 – 8 and No 9 will be produced in Autumn
2002. There were two editions for the first facsimile but they are both
now out of print and worth around £50 each. The same can be said of Nos 2
– 6 and no doubt the others will sell out too. In fact the originals are
probably more common than the facsimiles.

Girl Comic
No 1 2nd November 1951 VG £60 August 2001

Girls' Funnies
Possibly only one issue was published by Swan - 1949 VG plus £30 April 2001

Golden Fun
1939 & 1940 Good £25 December 2000

Granpop
1935 Hefty bump cover edge £20 April 2001
Nos 2 & 3 1948 & 1949 Good plus £10 April 2001

1949 VG £5 December 2000

Greyfriars Holiday
1920's x 6 annuals VG £80 November 2001
1931 & 1938 VG £35 each October 2000
1934 & 1940 G/VG £40 each October 2000
1937 & 1939 VG £10 each October 2000
1940 VG £40 October 2000

Happy Days
This scarce item was omitted from The Hamer Guide No 1 as a comic without an annual equivalent. However this Supplement has relaxed that rule. The comic published by Amalgamated Express began life in 1938. We sold 42 issues in Good only condition for £275 in February 2001 and have No 1 for sale in February 2002 for which we have applied an estimate of £300. We shall see.

Hobbies Weekly
No 1840 Mickey Mouse cover & free gift VG £65 August 2001

Hornet Comic
No 1 14th December 1963 (DC Thomson) VG plus £65 February 2001
Nos 1 – 13 G/VG £97 November 2001
1973 – 1975 Christmas issues VG £27 October 2001

Hotspur Book for Boys
1936 VG £35 August 2001
1936, 1939, 1941 & 1943 G/VG £45 August 2001

Hotspur Comic Paper
No 1 September 2nd 1933 Good only £120 August 2001
1933 – 1939 Christmas issues Good plus £42 October 2001
1940 – 1958 Christmas issues G/VG £50 October 2001
A good-sized collection 1930's trimmed comics £3 each April 2001
A good-sized collection 1940/50's trimmed comics £1.50 each April 2001
1950 – 1959 Fine in bound volumes £660 November 2001
New Hotspur No 1 24th October 1959 VG £40 February 2001

Hurricane Comic
No 1 February 29th 1964 Fine £40 February 2001

Invisible Dick
Written by Frank Topham & published by DC Thomson Good plus £45
August 2001

James Bond
1965 VG/Fine £15 October 2000
1966 VG/Fine £15 October 2000
1968 with 1967 Dr Who £55 December 2000

Japhet and Happy
1927 J & Co including Happy VG £22 October 2001
1928 J & The Arkubs VG £15 October 2001
1929 J & The Arkubs at Sea VG £12 October 2001
1930 J & Co on Arkub Island VG £22 October 2001
1933 – 1937 G/VG £70 October 2001
The above were published by Daily News/News Chronicle but there are also
About J & the Rest of the Noah Family published by Fleetgate in 1927 and
two books published by Cassell – Adventures of the Noah Family including
J & The Noahs on Holiday with J - All three Good £15 October 2001

Jester
1937 G/VG, 1938 G/VG, 1939 Good & 1940 Good £50 August 2001
1930's & 1940's x 5 annuals G/VG £80 December 2000

Jester Comic
My assessment of the early Jesters was proven to be wrong in a major way.
The comics are sought after by very few people but two of them got stuck
into the bidding for Lot 298 in February 2001. The Lot contained 7 bound
volumes from 1902 – 1905. The difficulty for the comic researcher is that
so little of the material was signed. However Jester in its early days had a
guest artist page and the artist did sign their work. Hence the incredible
scrap that ensued, the victor walking away with a hefty £2,100 plus
commission dent in their cheque book.

Jingles
1936 VG, 1938 G/VG, 1939 G/VG & 1941 Good £40 August 2001
1930's & 1940's x 5 annuals G/VG £80 December 2000

Jingles Comic
Approximately 150 x 1930's & 1940's comics VG £150 December 2001

Joe 90
1968 & 1969 G/VG £15 September 2001

Joe 90 Comic
See Lady Penelope

Jolly Comic
Bound volume 1937 Nos 129 – 154 VG £150 August 2001

Joy Book
1922 & 1923 VG £65 May 2000

Judy Comic
No 1 16th January 1960 VG plus £55 February 2001

June Comic
No 1 18th March 1961 Fine £22 February 2001

Kiddyfun
Perhaps there was no book for 1949 or 1944. Murdock Stimpson & Bert Hill
cover artwork. A VG collection £9 each April 2001

Kinema Comic
See Cheerio & Film Fun

Knock-out
1942 G/VG £40 October 2000, G/VG £75 August 2001
1943 G/VG £41 October 2000
1943 Reading copy & 1944 Good plus £80 August 2001
1944 Good only £31 October 2000
1945 Nr VG £41 October 2000, VG £75 August 2001
1946 Nr VG £41 October 2000, VG plus £35 August 2001
1947 G/VG £27 October 2000, VG plus £35 August 2001, Good plus £30
September 2001

1948 VG plus £27 August 2001, VG £32 September 2001
1949 VG plus £20 August 2001, G/VG £10 September 2001
1950 VG plus £20 August 2001
1951 & 1952 VG plus £40 August 2001
1953 – 1957 G/VG £27 August 2001
1952 – 1961 VG £30 August 2001

Knock-out Comic
No 1 VG £400 VG February 2001
No 5 Good £20 October 2001
Nos 8 & 10 Both Good £25 October 2001
Nos 23 – 26 Good £70 October 2001
1939 – 1944 Good plus £5 each October 2001
Bound volume Nos 175 – 200 1942 Good plus £130 April 2001

Lady Penelope
Lady Penelope Cool for Danger Novel VG in VG d/w with 1968 Annual £22
November 2001

Lady Penelope Comic
No 1 £90 February 2001 with Joe 90 & TV21 No 1's VG plus

Larks, The
No 1 published by Dalziel May 1st 1893 Good only £50 August 2001
No 1 New series published by Trapps Holmes June 7th 1902 Reading copy
£25 August 2001
300 issues between No 3 & No 300 Good £190 October 2001
Bound volumes x 2 1937 & 1940 VG £100 August 2001
These comic papers were published by Amalgamated Press from 1927.

Lawson Woods
Nos 1 & 2 1951 & 1952 G/VG £10 April 2001

Lion
1954 – 1959 G/VG £45 November 2001
1966 Fine £10 October 2000

Lion Comic
Barry Nelson wrote but did not draw Sandy Dean for this Amalgamated Press
publication from issue No 1. Artists would have included Bruce McDonald.
Nos 1 – 54 G/VG £95 December 2000
No 1 G/VG £90 November 2001
Nos 1, 3 & 5 VG £120 November 2001

Lot o'Fun Comic
No 1 March 17th 1906 Reading copy £12 August 2001

Louis Wain
1903 Summer Book Good only & worn Annual 1921 & Poor Rosebud 1907
£100 April 2001

Lucie Attwell, (Mabel Lucie Attwell)
1941 Little childish colouring VG £90 April 2001
1951 VG/Fine £40 September 2001
1961 VG £25 September 2001

Magic Fun Book
1941 Lacking spine £200 April 2001
1942 Taped spine G/VG £310 April 2001, Lacking spine cover £150
November 2001

Magic Comic
Flyer announcing imminent publication of Magic VG plus £100 August 2001
No 2 G/VG £75 September 2001
Nos 4 & 5 Reading copies £32 each October 2001
No 13 VG £65 October 2001
No 16 VG £105 October 2001
Nos 33 & 35 Good only £90 October 2001
No 38 G/VG £75 September 2001
No 42 VG with Poor 43 & 51 £40 October 2001
Nos 52 – 56 G/VG £150 October 2001
No 54 VG £70 September 2001
Nos 57 - 61 G/VG £170 October 2001
Nos 62 – 66 G/VG £190 October 2001
Nos 67 - 71 G/VG £140 October 2001
Nos 72 – 74 G/VG £100 October 2001
No 76 Good plus £40 September 2001

Man from UNCLE
1966 & 1967 Both Fine £20 October 2000

Merry & Bright
Bound Volumes x 4 between 1921 & 1933 VG plus £360 August 2001

Merry Maker
Published by Burns 1940's
Nos 1 – 11 G/VG £35 in February 2001

Merry Moments
All published by Newnes
No 1 Good plus £37 August 2001

Mickey Mouse – See Colour Plates Hamer Guide No 1
1930 Well worn example £255 April 2001
1931 VG plus £250 December 2000, VG £75 April 2001
1932 G/VG £65 April 2001
1933 Good only £35 April 2001
1934 G/VG £100 May 2000, Good only £40 April 2001
1936 Reading copy £17 April 2001
1937 G/VG £32 April 2001
1938 G/VG £22 April 2001
1939 Reading copy £30 April 2001
1940 Reading copy & 1943 £38 April 2001
1940 & 1941 VG £120 & £100 May 2000
1943 VG £60 May 2000
1944 Good & 1946 VG £35 April 2001

Mickey Mouse Other Titles
Adventures of MM published by Harrap 1931 Nr VG in chipped d/w £125 April 2001
MM and Pluto the Pup published by Collins 1936 G/VG £25 April 2001
Ein Lustiges Filmbildbuch 1930's VG £120 April 2001
Great Big Midget Books published by Dean 1930's G/VG £15 each April 2001
Movie Stories published by Dean 1931 Good only £55 April 2001
Movie Stories Book 2 published by Dean 1932 G/VG £35 April 2001
Mickey Mouse Merchandise catalogue 1938/39 VG £250 April 2001
Silly Symphony Annual 1937 VG plus in Poor d/w £70 April 2001

Mickey Mouse Weekly
1936 Nos 4 & 12 – 47 Good plus £110 September 2001
1937 Full year G/VG £125 September 2001
1938 Full year G/VG £105 September 2001
1939 Full year VG £105 September 2001
1940 Full year VG £155 September 2001
1941 Lacking 6 issues Good plus £75 September 2001
1944 – 1946 Full years & 18 issues 1943 Good plus £180 September 2001
Coronation issue 1952 Good plus £10 September 2001

Miller/Fawcett

& other publishers including Anglo Features, Arnold, Hutton, Pemberton, Westworld & World Distributors. These are usually 6d or 1/- reprints of US comics with black & white contents. Prices are per issue in VG based on prices realised in Hamer Auctions February, April, August, October, November & December 2001.

Ace Malloy (£2), All Space (£10), Annie Oakley (£4), Apache Kid (£4), Arrowhead (£6), Astounding Stories (£6), Atomic Mouse (£6), Battle (£5), Blackhawk (£5), Black Knight (£8), Black Magic (£8), Black Rider (£8), Blue Bolt (£6), British TV Heroes (£5), Buffalo Bill (£8), Bugs Bunny (£6), Captain Marvel (£10), Captain Midnight (£10), Captain Miracle (£20), Captain Valiant (£8), Captain Vigour (£5), Charlie Chan (£4), Cisco Kid (£6), Colorado Kid (£4), Daredevil (£6), Davy Crockett (£6), Dick Hercules (£2), Don Winslow (£4), Durango Kid (£6), Family Favourites (£4), Fantastic Tales (£8), Felix the Cat (£8), Fighting Marines (£6), Flash Gordon (£6), Flash (£6), Football (£5), Frontier Western (£4), Gene Autry (£5), Gunsmoke (£4), Hot Rods (£4), I Love Lucy (£3), Jim Bowie (£3), Joe Palooka (£6), John Wayne (£12), Jungle Jim (£20), King Comic (£4), Lone Ranger (£12), Lone Rider (£5), Lone Star (£4), Lorna the Jungle Girl (£20), Loony Toons (£3), Marvelman (£7 pre No 200 & £4 post No 200), Marvelman at War (£4), Marvelman Family (£7), Pancho Villa (£4), Pete Mangan of Space Patrol (£10), Mystery in Space (£20), Planet (£20), Plastic Man (£4), Police Files (£10), Popeye (WDL £5, Pemberton £3, Miller £7), Out of this World (£4), Range Rider (£5), Red Star (£4), Ringo Kid (£6), Robin Hood (£8), Rod Cameron (£6), Roy Carson (£10), Sam Hill (£10), Saint, The (£20), Secret Service (£10), Space Ace (£25), Space and Adventure (£10), Space Commander (£10), Space Commander Kerry (£10), Spaceman (£10), Spellbound (£4), Strange Worlds (£15), Tarzan (£3), Tim Holt (£4), Tom & Jerry (£2), TV Features (£15), Whizz (£10), Young Marvelman (£3)

The following Miller/Fawcett publications are of special interest:
Capt Marvel Junior Annual Spiral spine G/VG £32 December 2001
Captain Marvel Colouring Book 1941 VG £35 October 2001
Marvel Family No 1 1946 G/VG £80 October 2001
Whizz Comic No 1 VG £100 October 2001

Mrs Hippo's

1926 & 1928 G/VG £25 September 2001
1927 – 1932 Good plus £42 December 2000

Between 1929 & 1940 x 4 annuals Good £30 October 2001

Modern Boy
Annuals 1937 & 1938 G/VG £20 August 2001

Modern Boy Comic Paper
Biggles content x 35 issues Good plus £145 August 2001
Biggles content x 8 issues Good only £22 December 2001
No 294 Mickey Mouse cover & 8 others Good plus £12 August 2001

Monster Rupert
See Rupert Bear

Mounties Book
Published by DC Thomson 1939 G/VG £20 April 2001

New Funnies
Published by Swan 1940's
Nos 2 – 42 & 7 holiday specials G/VG £190 August 2001

Nipper
Also published 1941

Nister's Holiday
1913 G/VG £85 November 2001
1915 VG £60 May 2000

Okay Adventure
1958 Fine in d/w £10 October 2000

Oojah
No 1 1922 G/VG & 8 other annuals to 1951 £60 April 2001
1924 Good £24 September 2001
Oojah House was probably not an annual and the book was published by
Hulton Press 1923 – 1926. Although there has been some debate as to
whether a book was published for 1928 my correspondent says he has one
clearly dated by a previous owner. The first story is The Butterfly Express.
He goes on to say Pitkin published four annuals from 1949 – 1952 and that it
is likely from an editorial comment on the dustwrapper of the 1949 annual
that no issue appeared in 1942.

Oor Wullie

I somehow missed out the descriptions for the undated books in The Hamer Comic Annual Guide No 1. Here they are now:

1941 Wullie sitting on bucket Plain yellow background Reading copy £860 October 2000

1943 Wullie standing with conkers to hand, side glancing at the reader G/VG £1700 May 1999, Poor £180 April 2001

1949 Wullie's large portrait against bright red background Good only £270 October 2000

1951 Sixteen pictures of Wullie Fine £250 May 2000
1953 Twelve pictures of Wullie Fine £250 May 2000, G/VG £85 November 2001

1955 Wullie reading Oor Wullie, reading Oor Wullie
1957 Wullie sits in front of cabin Predominantly blue background Reading copy, 1959 Paint pot and brushes, 1961 About to tackle his breakfast, 1963 Policeman shadow, 1965 Shining the bucket & 1967 All VG £90 October 2000

1959 G/VG £32 December 2000
1963 VG £2 November 2001

A tiny pen and ink original by Dudley Watkins made £440 in April 2001.

Ovaltineys' Own

These lovely comics were published by Target.
Bound volume 1935 – 1939 VG/Fine £200 August 2001

Panda Comic

No 1 1949 British reprint of Dutch comic VG/Fine £170 August 2001

PC 49

A reader points out that PC 49 was written by Alan Stranks and not drawn by him as I claimed. The principal artist was John Worsley.

Phantom, The

No 1 published by WDL 1967 VG/Fine £15 April 2001

Picture Show
1929 VG £30 May 2000
1939 - 1941 in glicene d/ws £70 October 2001
1942 Nr VG £17 May 2000
1942, 1943 & 1961 G/VG £60 October 2001

Picture Show Magazine
No 1 1919 Reading copy £32 October 2001

Pip & Squeak
1923 VG £45 September 2001

Playbox
No 1 1909 £45 September 2001

Playbox Comic
18 x Christmas issues between 1925 & 1954 Good £45 October 2001

Playhour Comic
Issues from 1957/58 containing Hiawatha colour artwork are sought after and could run to £50 each in the right condition.

Playtime
1920's & 1930's annuals Good £4 each October 2001

Playtime Comic
No 1 March 29th 1919 VG £32 February 2001
1919 – 1923 34 issues G/VG £20 October 2001

Poppet
No 1 October 15th 1963 Fine £30 February 2001
There are also two different Clark Brandt prints from 1971 worth around £20 each in Fine.

Popeye
Popeye's cruise published by Birn Bros 1938 G/VG £25 April 2001

Puck
Four reading copies from the 1920's & 11 other annuals G/VG £15 April 2001
1938 G/VG & 1941 VG in VG d/w £32 September 2001

Radio Fun

1940 Good plus £40 May 2001, Poor £15 August 2001
1941 Good plus £30 August 2001
1942 Good £45 August 2001
1943 G/VG £55 October 2000, G/VG £82 August 2001
1944 G/VG £80 August 2001
1945 G/VG £42 October 2000, Good plus £42 April 2001, VG £55 August 2001

1946 VG £37 October 2000, G/VG £45 August 2001
1947 VG £32 May 2000, G/VG £17 October 2000, VG plus £45 August 2001

1948 VG £41 October 2000, VG/Fine £50 August 2001
1949 VG/Fine £65 August 2001
1950 Wilfred Pickles cover VG/Fine £45 August 2001
1951 VG plus & 1952 – 1954 G/VG £45 August 2001
1955 – 1959 G/VG £30 August 2001
1959 VG £15 October 2000
1950's & 1960's x 10 annuals G/VG £80 December 2000

Radio Fun Comic

No 1 G/VG £200 February 2001
Nos 5, 6 & 7 Good plus £70 October 2001
No 11 VG & Christmas 1939 G/VG £45 September 2001
Nos 18 VG, 19 Poor & 20 G/VG £45 September 2001
Nos 26 VG, 49 & 57 G/VG £40 September 2001
1930's Good plus x 26 issues £6 each October 2001
1940's and 1950's Good plus £2 each October 2001
1940 – 1944 x 40 issues Good £240 February 2001
1945 Complete year in bound volume VG £315 April 2001
1946 Complete year in bound volume VG £270 April 2001
1947 Complete year in bound volume VG £185 April 2001
1948 Complete year in bound volume VG £240 April 2001
1949 Complete year in bound volume VG £140 April 2001
Late 1940's & early 1950's Good plus £1.50 each May 2001
1940's & 1950's x 46 issues G/VG £140 September 2001

Rainbow

9 books between 1924 & 1955 Good plus £40 October 2001
17 annuals from 1920's – 1940's Good plus £70 December 2000

Rainbow Comic
No 1 February 14th 1914 Good £130 August 2001

Rattler Comic
The comics were published by Target from 1933.
Bound volumes x 4 1933 – 1938 Lacking No 1 VG £130 August 2001

Rawhide
Starred Clint Eastwood
1961 – 1964 (World Distributors) Estimated at £12 each
1962 (Television Story Book – Newtown) Estimated at £12

Robin Comic
No 1 VG £50 November 2001

Robin Hood Comics and Papers
Robin Hood Library No 1 Amalgamated Press 1919 & No 1 Aldine 1924 Good
£27 April 2001

Rocket Comic
This bright paper was published by The News of the World.
No 1 21st April 1956 G/VG £65 October 2001
Nos 2 – 20 G/VG £100 October 2001

Rover Book for Boys
No 1 1926 Good plus £85 August 2001
1928, 1929, 1933 - 1938, & 1956 G/VG £150 August 2001

1941 G/VG £20 April 2001

Rover Comic Paper
1922 Christmas issue VG £15 October 2001
1923 Christmas issue VG £25 October 2001
1920's & 1930's Christmas issues x 10 G/VG £60 October 2001
1941 – 1949 Christmas issues Good £42 October 2001

Roy Carson
See TV Boardman

Rupert Bear

This is not an exhaustive list but represents the books we have sold since May 2000. For a chronology of Rupert Bear titles to 1974 and colour plates see The Hamer Comic Annual Guide No 1.

The Annuals

1936 Good only £60 May 2000, Rebound in original boards £80 May 2000, Good only £80 October 2000 & Reading copy £60 October 2000, Bright copy sans d/w signed AE Bestall £400 October 2000, Fine in brittle & chipped d/w £1,100 May 2001,

1937 Reading copy £30 May 2000, VG plus £300 December 2000, VG plus £360 November 2001

1938 Rebound in original boards £80 May 2000, Nr VG £200 October 2000, Nr VG £180 December 2000, VG £300 November 2001

1940 VG/Fine £650 May 2000
1941 Good only £90 July 2001, Reading copy £40 September 2001
1942 Fine £800 May 2000, VG plus £500 May 2001
1943 Fine £600 May 2000, VG £225 May 2000, Good £200 May 2001, Good £65 September 2001

1944 G/VG £250 May 2000, G/VG £100 September 2001, VG £120 November 2001

1945 VG/Fine £300 November 2001, Red endpapers VG £200 November 2001

1946 G/VG £55 May 2000, Nr VG £140 October 2000, VG/Fine £150 May 2000, Nr VG £100 January 2001, G/VG £90 September 2001, VG £80 November 2001

1947 G/VG £55 May 2000, VG plus £120 May 2000, VG £100 January 2001, Nr VG £80 January 2001, Fine £260 May 2001, G/VG £70 September 2001, G/VG £60 November 2001, VG plus £140 November 2001

1948 VG £80 October 2000, Fine £125 December 2000, Fine £330 May 2001, VG/Fine £95 September 2001, G/VG £60 November 2001

1949 Fine £120 December 2000, VG/Fine £100 November 2001, VG plus £85 November 2001, VG £55 November 2001

1950 G/VG £50 May 2000, VG £75 September 2001, VG £80
September 2001

1951 VG plus £70 October 2000, G/VG £40 October 2000
1952 VG plus £60 October 2000
1953 Nr VG £52 October 2000
1954 G/VG £45 October 2000, VG/Fine £65 July 2001, G/VG £50
September 2001

1955 Fine £85 May 2000, Fine £100 October 2000, VG £60 October 2000,
G/VG £37 December 2000, Fine £155 May 2001

1956 Nr Fine £60 October 2000, £120 Fine £200 October 2000, G/VG
£42 December 2000, G/VG £32 September 2001

1957 Nr Fine £60 May 2000, VG plus £75 October 2000, Fine £150
October 2000, Page missing £35 October 2000, G/VG £60 July 2001

1958 Fine £160 October 2000, G/VG £32 December 2000
1959 Fine £100 October 2000, G/VG £30 December 2000, G/VG £42
July 2001

1960 MP untouched Fine/Mint £320 October 2000, MP undone Fine £130
October 2000

1961 MP untouched Mint £330 October 2000, MP untouched Fine £150
October 2000, VG £40 December 2000

1962 VG plus One MP done £50 July 2001, MP untouched Fine £160
October 2000, Nr VG £32 December 2000

1963 MP untouched Fine £160 October 2000, One MP done VG £40
December 2000, MP hardly touched Fine £100 July 2001, VG plus MP done
£50 July 2001

1964 MP untouched Mint £150 October 2000, VG £22 December 2000, MP
untouched Fine £150 July 2001, MP untouched VG £100 July 2001

1965 MP half done VG £22 December 2000
1965 G/VG & 1966 Good £55 September 2001

1966 MP done VG £60 May 2000, MP untouched Mint £250 October 2000,
MP untouched VG £55 December 2000

1967 MP untouched Mint £190 October 2000, MP untouched VG £90
December 2000

1968 MP undone Fine £100 May 2000, MP untouched Mint £150 October 2000
1969 Mint £90 October 2000
1968 – 1973 G/VG £25 October 2000
1969 – 1976 VG £45 November 2001
1973 Rare brown-faced printing Fine £16,500 May 2000

Early Collectable Rupert Books
The Adventures of Rupert Little Lost Bear Good plus £350 May 2000, Good
only £180 May 2000, Good only £140 December 2000, VG/Fine £950 May
2001, Respined VG £460 November 2001

Little Bear and the Ogres Good only £200 May 2000
Little Bears Adventures No 1 1924 Good only £200 May 2000, VG plus
£1,050 May 2001

Monster Rupert – the original series
1931 Restored VG £170 December 2000
1932 G/VG £300 May 2000
1933 Lacking spine £80 October 2000, Reading copy £40 December 2000
1934 Spine overlaid £100 October 2000, Facsimile endpapers, spine & rear
board £80 October 2000

Rupert Little Bear Series
I had quite forgotten until a Chichester customer reminded me that we had
sold a copy of Rupert and Reynard Fox a few years ago. The book published
by Sampson Low, Marston in 1925 was omitted from the Hamer Comic Annual
Guide No 1. It must be scarce however as we have not seen one since.
Rupert and the Old Miser Lacking front endpaper Good plus £150
November 2001
Rupert and the Princess VG plus £520 May 2000, Good £250
November 2001
Rupert and the Magic Key/Brigands VG with publisher's insert £950
November 2001

Scarce Rupert Titles
1938 Rupert Story Book G/VG £50 January 2001
1939 Rupert Little Bear More Stories Reading copy £40 December 2000
1940 Rupert Again VG plus £340 May 2000, G/VG £200 May 2000, VG £350 May 2000

And Not So Scarce
1944 Rupert Little Bear More Stories reprint VG £35 September 2001
1948 Monster Rupert G/VG in d/w £60 May 2000
1954 The New Rupert Colour Adventure Book & 3 other reprints VG £43 September 2001

1955 Rupert Adventure Book Fine £50 May 2000

Pop-Ups – Daily Express Children's
1930 Worn £30 May 2000
1934 Spine overlaid G/VG £70 May 2000, VG £150 September 2001

Rupert Little Bear Library
No 1 1st edition Good plus £32 October 2000
No 2 1st edition Fine in d/w £160 December 2000
Nos 2, 3 & 4 1st editions lacking original spines £20 October 2000
Nos 5 & 6 1st editions G/VG £35 October 2000
Nos 7, 8 & 9 1st editions in G/VG d/ws £200 May 2000
No 12 1st edition VG/Fine in chipped d/w £140 December 2000
Nos 13, 14 & 15 1st editions VG/Fine in G/VG d/ws £280 May 2000
No 16 1st edition Fine in chipped d/w £170 December 2000
Nos 16, 17 & 18 1st editions including 1 reprint VG/Fine in G/VG d/ws £260 May 2000
Nos 19 – 23 1st editions including 2 reprints VG/Fine in G/VG d/ws £230 May 2000
Nos 22, 23, 24 & 27 reprints inc 1 1st edition VG/Fine in G/VG d/ws £100 May 2000
Nos 25 & 28 1st editions VG/Fine in G/VG d/ws £190 May 2000
Nos 29 – 33 including 2 reprints & 2 1st editions in d/ws G/VG £170 May 2000
No 30 1st edition Fine in chipped d/w £150 December 2000
No 34 1st edition in d/w & 9 reprints 36 – 44 G/VG £200 May 2000
No 26 1st edition VG/Fine in chipped d/w £120 October 2000
No 45 Lacking spine & 46 Good plus 1st editions £60 October 2000
1970's Reprints Nos 1 – 18 Mint £47 May 2000

Rupert Adventure Series
No 1 VG £40 November 2001
Nos 1 - 19 VG £240 May 2000
Nos 1, 3, 5 & 11 All Fine £85 May 2001
Nos 3, 5 , 7 & 11 VG £67 November 2001
No 10 Fine £75 May 2001, VG £35 November 2001
Nos 20 – 29 VG £100 May 2000
Nos 30 – 35 with 34 Poor £115 November 2001
Nos 30 – 48 VG £320 October 2000
Nos 36 – 39 VG plus £130 November 2001
No 40 Fine £60 November 2001
No 41 Fine £32 November 2001
No 42 Fine £32 November 2001
No 43 Fine £70 November 2001
No 45 VG plus £50 November 2001
No 45 Fine £45 May 2001, Fine £37 November 2001
No 46 VG £35 November 2001
Nos 46, 47 & 48 £85 September 2001
Nos 47 & 48 Good £47 November 2001
No 48 VG £60 May 2001, VG £35 November 2001
No 49 VG £60 May 2000, VG £65 December 2000, Good only £70 May 2001, VG £50 September 2000, Good plus £45 November 2001
No 50 Fine £110 May 2000, VG £65 September 2000

Similar Publications
Rupert Activity Book – Music and Story Book No 1 published by Odhams January 1958 VG/Fine £1,600 May 2001
Rupert Activity Book No 2 VG £20 May 2000
Rupert Music Book No 2 G/VG £250 January 2001

Famous Yellow Library
The pair made only £20 May 2000 & £30 May 2001

Rupert and the Wonderful Boots
Nr VG £20 May 2000

Cut-Outs
Rupert and the Snow Man 1950 Fine £300 May 2000
Rupert and Edward and the Circus 1949 Nr VG £90 May 2000

LTA Robinson Publications
Rupert Gets Captured Worn spine edge G/VG £1050 May 2001
Rupert at the Seaside Nr VG £65 May 2000
Facsimile Rupert Annuals
1936 Fine in d/w £60 May 2000, Fine in d/w £80 April 2001, Fine in d/w
£75 July 2001

1937 Fine £60 May 2001
1938 Fine £60 September 2001
1939 & 1940 Fine £38 September 2001
1941 & 1942 Fine £62 September 2001
1942 & 1943 Fine £65 September 2001
1942 Fine £47 July 2001
1943 & 1945 Fine £55 September 2001
1945 Fine £32 July 2001
1948 & 1949 Fine £28 September 2001

Rupert Ephemera
Cutlery Set 1972 Fine in box £120 September 2001
Daily Express Children's Club Captain's badge £85 May 2000
Linen Calendar 1973 Fine £42 May 2000
National Westminster cheque for £1 Fine £17 May 2000
Poster by Pace International 1970 G/VG £170 May 2000
Wedgwood 1 pint mug Boxed £155 October 2000
Wendy House 1981 in Poor box £70 October 2000
Wedgwood plates with 1949 & 1961 covers Perfect £100 October 2000
Wedgwood plate 1961 cover £90 November 2001
Storey's Wallpaper shop display £65 October 2000
Clark Brandt Prints 1948, 49, 64, 67, 68 & 69 Covers Fine £70 each May 2000
Linen Rupert Calendar 1972 Fine £42 May 2000
There are two birthday cards – one showing Rupert posting a letter, the
other Rupert with a paint tin. There is also a Christmas card which sold for
£75 in May 2000.

School Friend
1935 & 1936 both in d/ws £70 May 2000
See Schoolgirls' Own

School Friend Comic
No 1 May 17th 1919 Good plus £50 August 2001
No 1 (New Series) Less than VG £65 February 2001

Nos 1 – 33 in bound volume 1950 VG/Fine £170 August 2001

Schoolgirls Picture Library
A small collection published by Amalgamated Press made £3 each April 2001.

Schoolgirls Own
1927, 1927(School Friend) & 1934 £17 April 2001

Scramble Comic
Nos 1 – 53 in two bound volumes 1949 – 1950 VG £60 August 2001

Serenade
No 1 September 22nd 1962 Fine £15 February 2001

Sexton Blake
1938 Nr VG & 1939 Good £80 December 2000

Sherlock Holmes
See Super Detective Library

Skipper Book for Boys
1932 G/VG £40 August 2001
1933 Good plus £20 August 2001
1935 G/VG £30 August 2001
1936 Good plus £30 August 2001
1937 Reading copy £30 August 2001
1939 G/VG & 1948 VG £30 August 2001
1941 Good plus £25 August 2001
1942 Reading copy £10 April 2001

Skipper Comic Paper
1930 – 1940 Christmas issues Good plus £100 October 2001

Slick Fun
1949 – 1951, 1953, 1954 & 1956 G/VG £55 September 2001

Snow White & Rose Red
Published by John Leng in soft covers 1940 G/VG £60 April 2001

Sparky Comic
1966 – 1975 Christmas issues VG £30 October 2001

Speed
1937 Mountie trying to grab rope ladder from plane

Spirit, The
See TV Boardman

Sports Fun
No 1 New series May 13th 1922 G/VG £40 August 2001
See Film Fun

Sun Comic
Bound volume 1952 – 1953 Nos 164 – 229 Fine £130 February 2001

Sunbeam
1935 G/VG £10 September 2001

Super-Cinema
All were published by Amalgamated Press in dustwrappers.
1952 (Lex Barker Cover) Estimated at £12

Super Detective Library
Buck Ryan between Nos 156 & 186 VG £4 each April 2001
Sherlock Holmes Nos 65 & 74 G/VG £20 each April 2001
The Saint No 15 & Bulldog Drummond No 13 G/VG £30 April 2001

Superman
1954/55 VG £30 November 2001

Superman Comics
See Batman

Superthriller
There is clear interest in this series first published by Foldes but taken
over by WDL at issue No 11 (although still printed by Foldes) and bidding
was brisk in April 2001 when a small collection was sold in our rooms at
around £10 each VG.

Swan War & Western Comics
These were American comics reprinted by the enterprising Gerald Swan
who had bought a huge stockpile of paper before the shortages during the
war and reaped the benefit of his far sightedness by keeping going as

others struggled.
VG £5 each December 2001

Swift Comic
No 1 March 24th 1954 G/VG £22 August 2001, VG £32 November 2001

Swift Morgan
See TV Boardman

Tales of Wells Fargo
1961 (Card covers No 1 – World Distributors) Estimated £10
1963 – 1964 (World Distributors) Estimated £12
1962 (Big TV Bumper Book – Peverill) Estimated £12

Teddy Tail
Pen & ink originals by Herbert Foxwell & Arthur Potts (Spot) made £120 &
£50 respectively in February 2001
A Tony Hawes 1947 watercolour and Potts pen & ink original made £200 in
April 2001.

Tenderfoot
Also known as Sugarfoot in USA and featured Will Hutchins.
1961 (Dean) Estimated at £12
1962 – 1963 (World Distributors) Estimated at £8 each

Three Men in a Tub
Published by DC Thomson G/VG £90 December 2000

Thrill Comic
Published by Swan 1940's.
Nos 2 – 14, 16, 18 – 20, 22 – 23 & 3 holiday specials G/VG £80 August 2001

Thriller, The
No 1 February 9th 1929 Reading copy £17 August 2001
A worn collection of 24 issues between 1929 & 1940 £85 April 2001.

Thriller Picture Library
A collection between Nos 54 & 235 £3 each G/VG April 2001

Thunderbirds
1966 Fine £17 October 2000

Tiger Comic
No 1 VG with Free space gun £160 November 2001

Tiger Tim, Tiger Tim's Weekly
12 books between 1922 & 1956 Good £40 October 2001

Tiger Tim's Tales No 1 pub Amalgamated June 1919 as The Magic Milestone
in A5 landscape format VG £55 February 2001
Dick in Fairy Land June 1919 VG £30 February 2000
1930's x 12 issues Wonderland Tales Good £32 October 2001

Tiny Tots Comic
Nos 2 – 283 G/VG £235 October 2001

Toby Twirl
There are actually four large format books:
Toby Twirl and The Mermaid Princess
Toby Twirl in Pogland (Not Pogoland!)
Toby Twirl and the Magic Ring (2 inches smaller)
Toby Twirl Rescues Prince Apricot VG £100 December 2001

There were two Toby Twirl pop-up books
Dilly Paddle & Pirate both published by Sampson Low

Other Toby Twirl books of note are:
The Toby Twirl Colour Strip Adventure Book (1953)
The New Toby Twirl Colour Strip Adventure Book (1954)
Toby Twirl on Dapple Heath (1954)
Toby Twirl and The Talking Poodle 1954
LTA Robinson produced two Magic Painting Books – Merry Magic & Jolly Magic

Toddler's Treasure
Published by John Leng
1929 – 1931 Good plus £20 August 2001
1930 G/VG £5 August 2001

Topical Funnies
Published by Swan 1940's
Nos 1 – 5 including 1A & 9 – 24 & 5 holiday specials G/VG £200 August 2001

Topper Book
1955 An unusually large card covered natural history book reprinting 16 pages from Topper comic in February 1955 Good plus £24 May 2001

1960's Complete run VG £27 December 2000

Topper Comic
Bound volume Nos 1 – 52 VG £420 August 2001
24 x Christmas issues 1953 – 1973 G/VG £130 October 2001

Trains
Someone objected to trains being included in the Hamer Guide as they are not comic related. Someone else of a more train spottery inclination pointed out that the Trains Annual began as early as 1947 and ran until 1967 when its name changed to Trains.

Triumph
1937 & 1938 Good only £25 October 2001

Triumph Comic Paper
No 1 October 18th 1924 Good plus £50 August 2001
Eighteen issues had Superman covers. We sold seventeen of them in G/VG for £600 October 2001 so they are worth around £40 each but you would have to pay a lot more for VG.
1920's & 1930's Non-Superman issues Good only £1 each October 2001

25 Stories for Boys
Published by DC Thomson 1940 VG plus £20 April 2001

TV Boardman Comics
Various titles including Blackhawk, The Spirit, Buffalo Bill, Swift Morgan & Roy Carson. We sold 40 issues in less than VG for £640 in February 2001.

The publishers were also responsible for:
Feature Comics x 3 issues Good only £85 October 2001
Mystery Comics No 7 Good plus & No 11 Reading copy £25 October 2001

TV Century 21
See Lady Penelope

TV Century 21 Comic
1960's & 1970's x 11 issues G/VG £35 October 2001

TV Comic Comic
No 1 September 19th 1953 VG £27 December 2000
Bound volume 1951 – 1953 from No 2 VG/Fine £280 August 2001

TV Mini Books
Published by TV Comic in the late 1950's VG £7 each April 2001

TV 21 Comic
No 1 6th January 1968 £90 February 2001 with Lady Penelope & Joe 90 No 1's in VG plus
1960's x 37 issues VG £150 November 2001

TV Express
Issued after Express for Boys was renamed in 1960
1961 – 1962 Estimated at £8 each

TV Fun
No 1 September 19th 1953 VG £80 August 2001
Nos 2 – 5 G/VG £30 October 2001
1950's G/VG £1.50 each October 2001
1957 – 1960 (TV Fan from 1959 & then merged with Valentine 1960)

TV Land Comic
No 1 October 1st 1960 VG £22 February 2001

TV Picture Stories
A collection of 36 issues VG £220 April 2001

2000AD
Nos 1 – 4 plus a quantity VG/Fine £120 November 2001
Nos 1 – 30 VG plus £110 November 2001

Valiant Comic
No 1 6th October 1962 VG £70 February 2001

Victor
1968 & 1969 Both Fine £20 October 2000

Victor Comic
No 1 25th February 1961 Fine £80 February 2001
1962 – 1986 Christmas issues VG £45 October 2001
1961 – 1985 Non-special issues x 45 VG £23 October 2001
1964 & 1965 Full years VG £100 November 2001

Wagon Train
1960 (10 page Storybook – Purnell) Estimated at £12
1962 (Big TV Bumper Book – Peverill) Estimated at £15

Walt Disney
Snow White Annual 1938 Bright example with defunct book worm £60 April 2001
Snow White Annual 1938 Colouring to a few pages £80 with Snow White and The Seven Dwarfs G/VG published by Dean in soft covers 1938 G/VG April 2001

War Lord Comics
No 1 x 4 issues 1974 Mint with free gift £100 November 2001

Wells Fargo
See Tales of Wells Fargo

Wham! Comic
No 1 20th June 1964 Fine £35 February 2001

Whiskers
1948 – 1952 G/VG £20 August 2001
1949 & 1950 VG £27 September 2001

Whizzbang
A number of people have written to me suggesting my original guide price of £12 each was way off the mark and I agree with them.
1942 & 1943 (Amalgamated Press) would probably make £70 each.

Willie Waddle
1929 G/VG £10 August 2001
1932 Good & 1936 Reading copy £10 August 2001
1937 VG plus £22 August 2001
1938 Fine £30 August 2001
1948, 1949, 1950 & 1954 Soft covered annuals VG £75 August 2001

1949 Willie & ducklings in Heath Robinson contraption
1950 Willie & friends sledging from school
1954 Willie and friends sailing on beach

Wizard Book for Boys
No 1 1036 G/VG £55 August 2001
1938, 1939, 1942, & 1949 Good plus £45 August 2001

Wizard Comic Paper
1928 – 1929 Christmas issues Good plus £12 October 2001
1932 – 1939 Christmas issues Good only £30 October 2001
1940 – 1962 Christmas issues G/VG £70 October 2001

The Truth about Wilson by WSK Webb was published by DC Thomson in paperback Red Lion Series Nr VG £70 May 2001

Wizard Holiday Book
1939 Crowded cable car/fair ground scene
1938 & 1939 in Poor and Good respectively £60 April 2001

Wonder Comic
See Comic Cuts
1946/47 & 1952/53 in two bound volumes VG £115 December 2001

Wonderland
Published by World Educational Press
No 1 September 15th 1961 Fine £17 February 2001

Yogi Bear's Own Weekly
The comic was published by City Magazines.
No 1 27th October 1962 Fine £25 February 2001

Young Airman's
1942 G/VG £20 October 2001

Zoom
1941 Published DC Thomson Good only £10 April 2001